John Kember

Just for Two

16 Easy Piano Duets

ED 13383
ISMN M-2201-3245-2
ISNB 978-1-84761-252-6

www.schott-music.com

Mainz · London · Berlin · Madrid · New York · Paris · Prague · Tokyo · Toronto
© 2010 SCHOTT MUSIC Ltd, London · Printed in Germany

ED 13383
British Library Cataloguing-in-Publication Data
A catalogue record for this book is available from the British Library
ISMN M-2201-3245-2
ISBN 978-1-84761-252-6

Music setting by Darius Heise-Krzyszton, www.notensatzstudio.de
Printed in Germany S&Co.8708

Contents

Preface

For pianists, making music can often be a lonely pleasure. Duets provide a great way for the pianist to enjoy the benefits of ensemble, playing with other musicians, and the chance to share the enjoyment of music-making. They give the pianist the opportunity to explore new music, to help good time-keeping and to assist in playing expressively. Most importantly, they encourage players to listen to each other and blend together.

Duets also offer a wide range of fresh material, from arrangements of both traditional and modern 'classics', to original compositions both old and new. This set of original works brings together a wide variety of styles, Waltzes and Lullabies, to Jazz, Latin and Folk. The pieces are progressive in order of difficulty, and may be played by the teacher and pupil together, or provide a challenge for two players of equal ability.

Préface

Pour le pianiste, faire de la musique reste souvent un plaisir solitaire. Les duos sont un moyen fantastique de profiter des bénéfices de l'ensemble, ou jouer avec d'autres musiciens, et offrent la possibilité de partager le plaisir de faire de la musique. Ils donnent au pianiste l'occasion d'explorer de nouveaux répertoires, l'aident à conserver le bon tempo et à jouer de manière expressive. Plus important encore, ils encouragent les instrumentistes à s'écouter les uns les autres et à se fondre.

Les duos proposent également une grande variété de matériaux nouveaux, en partant d'arrangements de « classiques » à la fois traditionnels et modernes jusqu'à des compositions originales, récentes ou anciennes. Ce recueil d'œuvres originales réunit de nombreux styles différents, de la valse à la berceuse en passant par le jazz, la musique latino-américaine et le folk. Les pièces sont classées par ordre croissant de difficulté et peuvent être jouées par le professeur et l'élève ensemble ou constituer pour deux instrumentistes de niveau égal un joli défi à surmonter.

Vorwort

Für Pianisten ist das Musizieren oft ein einsames Vergnügen. Daher sind Duette eine hervorragende Möglichkeit, die Vorzüge des Zusammenspiels mit anderen Musikern zu genießen und die Freude am Musizieren zu teilen. Duette geben dem Pianisten die Möglichkeit, neue Musikstücke zu entdecken, den Takt gut zu halten und ausdrucksvoll zu spielen. Vor allem aber fördern sie das gegenseitige Zuhören und ein gutes Zusammenspiel.

Darüber hinaus bieten Duette eine große musikalische Bandbreite, von Bearbeitungen traditioneller und moderner „Klassiker" bis zu alten und neuen Originalkompositionen. Diese Sammlung mit Originalwerken vereint viele verschiedene Stilrichtungen: von Walzern und Wiegenliedern über Jazz bis zu Latin und Folk. Die Stücke sind nach aufsteigendem Schwierigkeitsgrad geordnet und können entweder vom Lehrer und Schüler oder aber von zwei Spielern derselben Spielstufe gespielt werden.

Secondo

1. Petite Valse

John Kember

S&Co. 8708

1. Petite Valse

John Kember

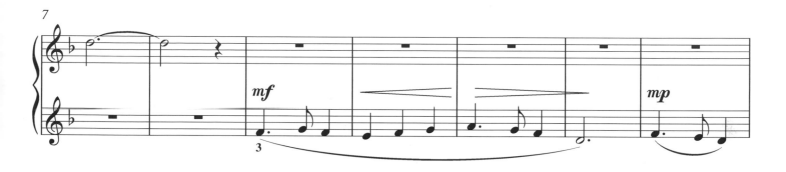

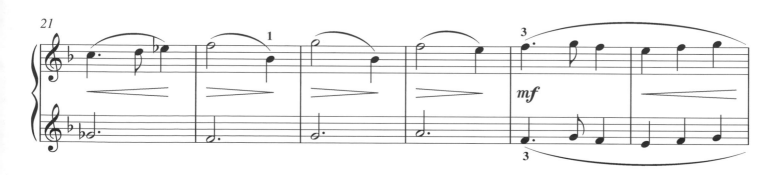

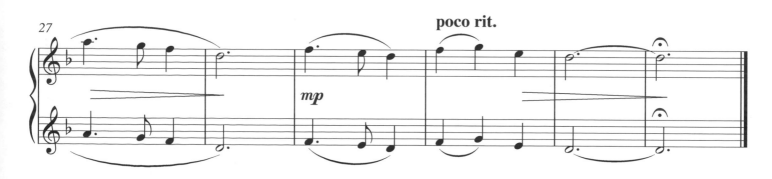

2. Berceuse

2. Berceuse

3. Barcarolle

4. Running Wild

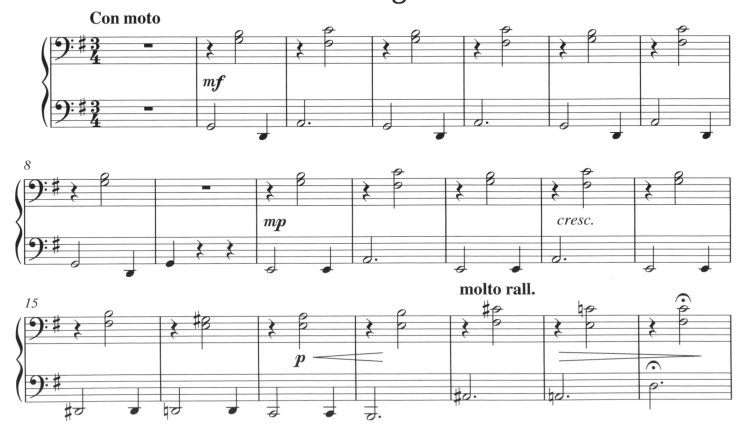

3. Barcarolle

4. Running Wild

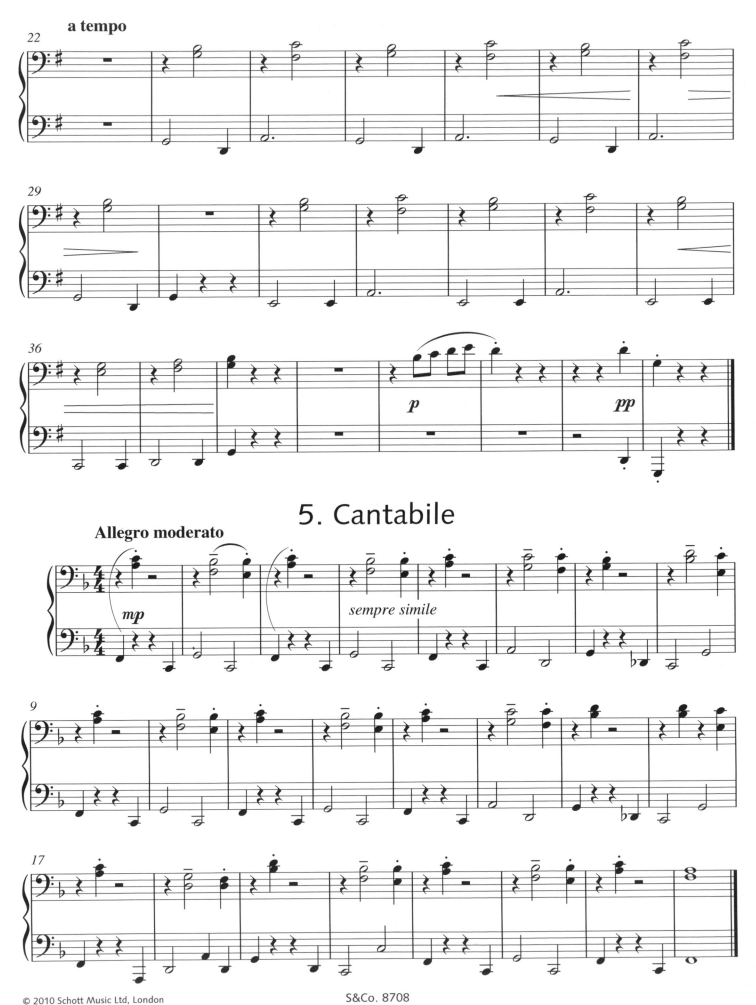

5. Cantabile

5. Cantabile

6. Habanera

6. Habanera

7. Folk Song

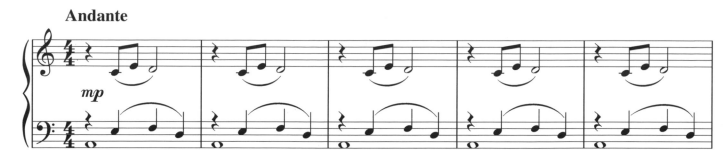

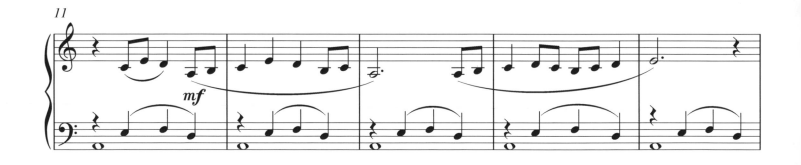

7. Folk Song

Secondo

8. Adagio

Slow and sustained

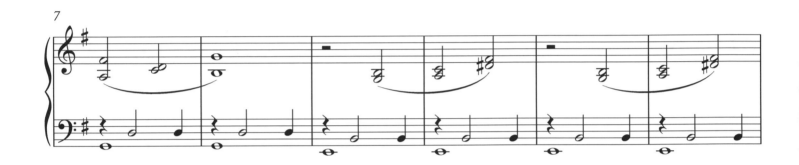

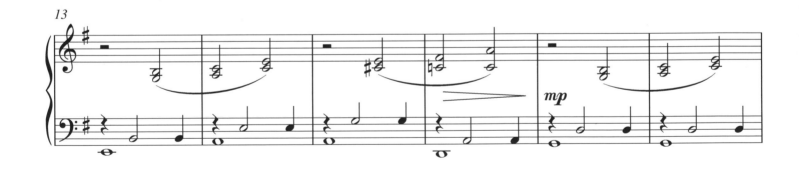

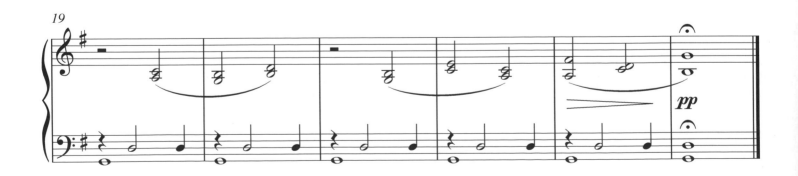

8. Adagio

Slow and sustained

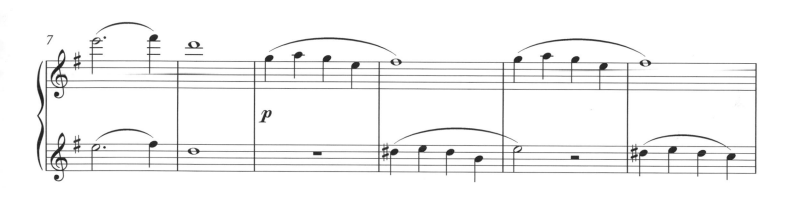

9. Song Without Words

9. Song Without Words

Secondo

10. Jazz Waltz

10. Jazz Waltz

Secondo

11. Blues for Two

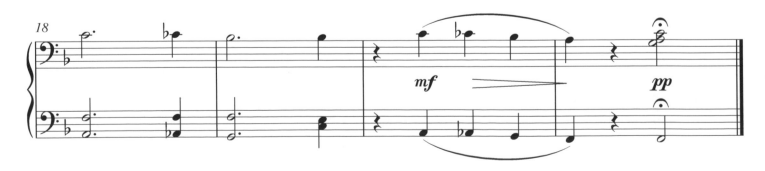

11. Blues for Two

Secondo

12. Drive Time

12. Drive Time

Secondo

13. Tropic Nights

Spiritoso, con rubato

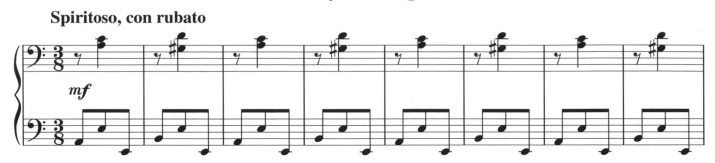

13. Tropic Nights

14. Romanza

Primo

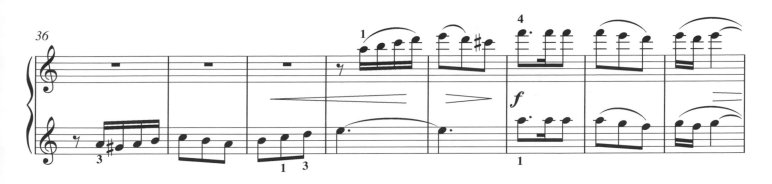

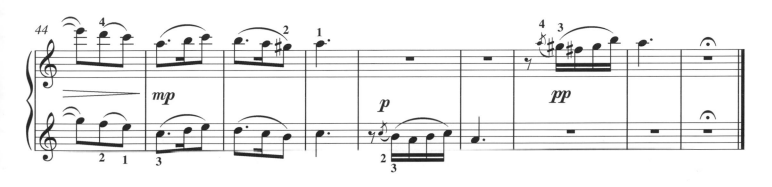

14. Romanza

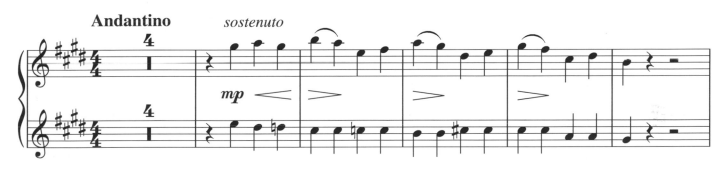

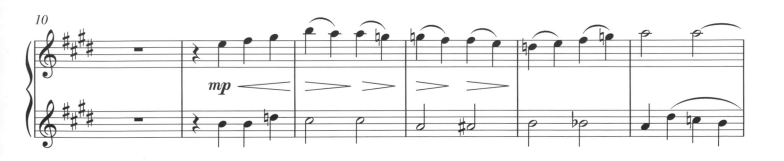

15. Cake Walk

15. Cake Walk

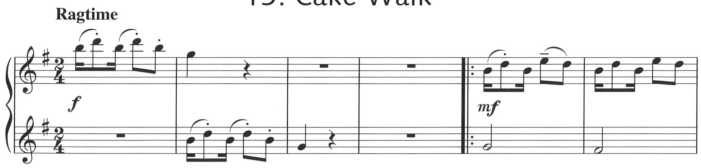

Secondo

16. Bossa Nova

Allegro moderato

16. Bossa Nova

Secondo

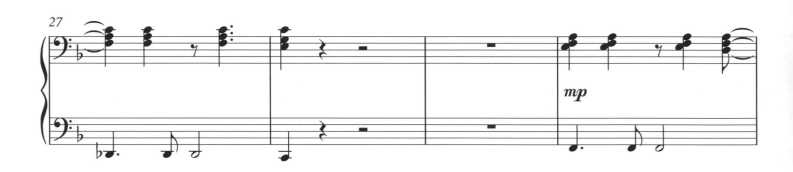

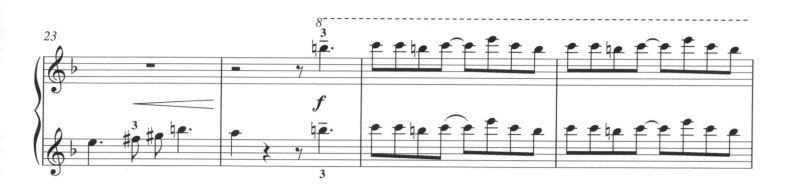

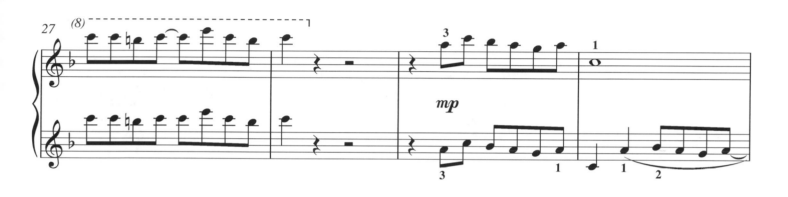

poco a poco dim.

sub. **f**

More Piano Titles from Schott Music

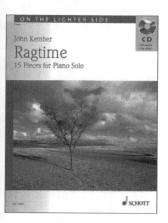

Ragtime
John Kember
ED 12890

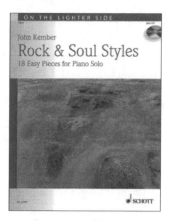

Rock & Soul Styles
John Kember
ED 12789

Solo Collection
John Kember
ED 12841

Duet Collection
John Kember
ED 12842

Klassik meets Jazz
Uwe Korn
ED 20177

Piano Sight-Reading 3
John Kember
ED 12889

Let's Play Together
Eduard Pütz
ED 8482

Jazz For Two, Vol. 1
Mike Schoenmehl
ED 7990

Water Music & Music for the Royal Fireworks
Handel/Heumann
ED 20658

Playing Latin Piano
Gabriel Bock
ED 9262

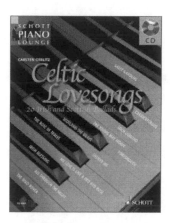

Celtic Lovesongs
Carsten Gerlitz
ED 9983

Piano for Christmas
Barrie Carson Turner
ED 12731

John Kember

Sight-Reading
A fresh approach

- Carefully-graded pieces, which are orginal tunes rather than abstract exercises
- Duets and accompanied pieces included to encourage ensemble playing
- New keys, rhythms and techniques introduced gradually

Vol 1 - ED 12737
Vol 2 - ED 12790

Vol 1 - ED 12836
Vol 2 - ED 12837

Vol 1 - ED 12956
Vol 2 - ED 12967

Vol 1 - ED 12954
Vol 2 - ED 12965

Vol 1 - ED 12817
Vol 2 - ED 12818

Vol 1 - ED 12953
Vol 2 - ED 12964

Vol 1 - ED 12834
Vol 2 - ED 12835

Vol 1 - ED 13053
Vol 2 - ED 13054

Vol 1 - ED 12736
Vol 2 - ED 12791
Vol 3 - ED 12889
More - ED 13318

Vol 1 - ED 12957
Vol 2 - ED 12968

Vol 1 - ED 12955
Vol 2 - ED 12966

SCHOTT
www.schott-music.com